Christmas Time

The First Christmas

Miles KeLLY

A long time ago, a young woman called Mary lived in the little town of Nazareth. She was engaged to marry a carpenter named Joseph.

One day, Mary was visited by an angel, who told her that she would have a very special baby. The baby would be the son of God, and he was to be called Jesus.

The angel also visited Joseph in a dream.

"Mary's child will be the saviour of God's people," the angel told him.

"You should raise him as your own."

Just before the birth, Mary and Joseph had to travel to Bethlehem, Joseph's birthplace, to be counted in a survey.

It was a very long way to
Bethlehem, and when they arrived it
was late. The streets were crowded with
people who had also come to be counted.

Mary and Joseph began to look
for somewhere to stay,

as the baby was about
to be born.

They tried the first inn they came to, but the innkeeper turned them away. He had no room to spare.

Mary and Joseph tried another inn, but again they were turned away.

Growing desperate,
Mary and Joseph went
from inn to inn – but
everywhere was full.

Eventually, they came to
the very last one.

"I'm sorry," the innkeeper said,
"but I don't have any rooms left.

All I can offer you is my stable."

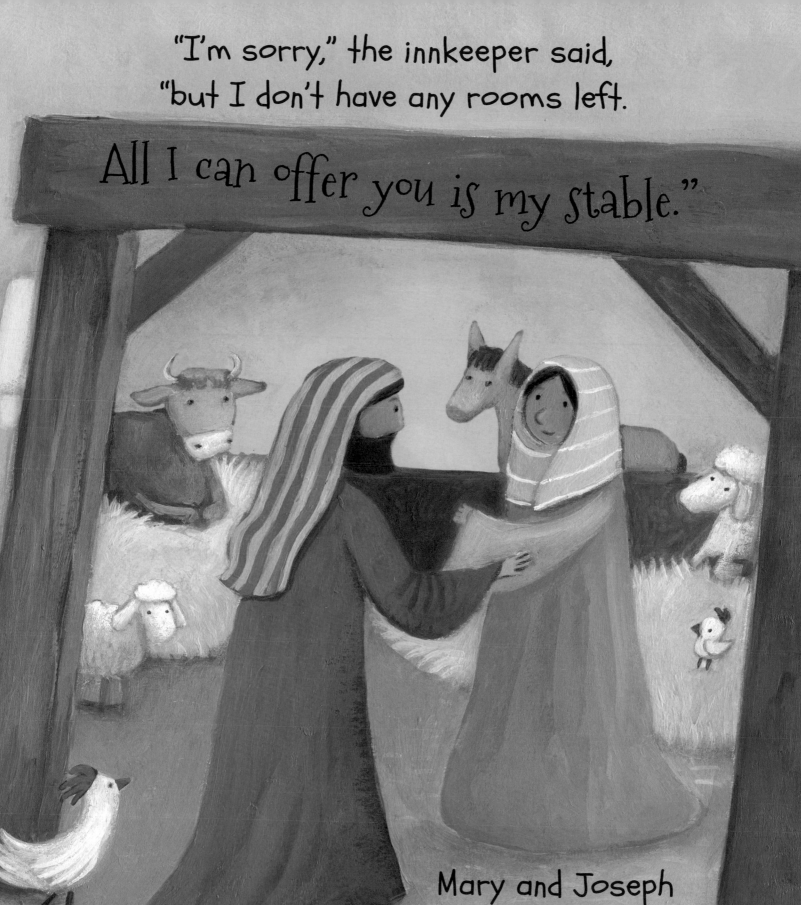

Mary and Joseph
were very grateful.

That night, in the warm stable amongst the animals, Mary gave birth to a baby boy.

She called him Jesus, just as the angel had said. Carefully, she wrapped him in cloths and laid him in the

manger.

Meanwhile, on the hills just outside Bethlehem, some shepherds were watching over their flock.

Suddenly, an angel appeared.
"I bring wonderful news.
A child has been born who will
be the saviour of all people."

As the shepherds watched, amazed, the sky was filled with hundreds of

dazzling angels

all singing

songs of joy.

The angel told the shepherds that they would find the baby in a stable in Bethlehem. They hurried straight there, very excited.

When they reached the stable, there was **Jesus** in the **manger**. The shepherds believed that he truly was the saviour.

Some time after Jesus was born, in distant lands, three wise men saw a new star in the night sky. It shone much more brightly than the rest.

They knew what this meant – a child had been born who would be the king of God's people.

They set off at once to find him, following the new star.

In Jerusalem, the wise men were summoned to see King Herod. He had heard about the new king, and was not happy.

He ordered them to tell him where the baby was once they had found him.

When the wise men reached Bethlehem, the star shone above a small house. Inside, the wise men bowed before Jesus and gave him gifts of gold, frankincense and myrrh.

On their journey home, the wise men did not return to King Herod, as they had a dream that warned them not to.

An angel then appeared to Joseph to warn him of danger, so the family set off for Egypt. There Jesus, the saviour, would be safe.